Dedicated
to Jesus Christ,
our Risen KING

Library of Congress Control Number: 2016960629

Original edition published in Denmark under the title *The Life of Jesus* by Scandinavia Publishing House, Copenhagen, Denmark. Copyright ©, Scandinavia Publishing House.

Edition copyright © 2017, Daughters of St. Paul

Published by Pauline Books & Media, 50 Saint Pauls Avenue, Boston, MA 02130-3491

www.pauline.org

Printed in China

LJGN ABCCHIDONJN1-24100007 4592-2

Pauline Books & Media is the publishing house of the Daughters of St. Paul, an international congregation of women religious serving the Church with the communications media.

1 2 3 4 5 6 7 8 9   21 20 19 18 17

The life of JESUS
A GRAPHIC NOVEL

CONCEPT AND ILLUSTRATIONS BY
JOSÉ PÉREZ MONTERO

TEXT BY BEN ALEX

Pauline
BOOKS & MEDIA

Contents

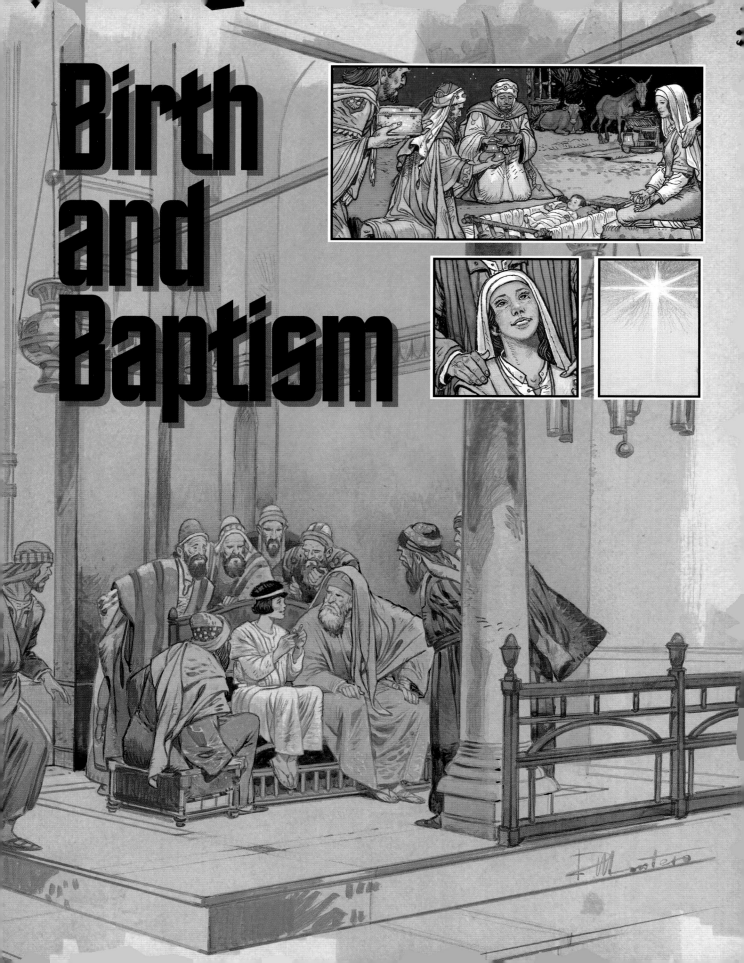

Birth and Baptism

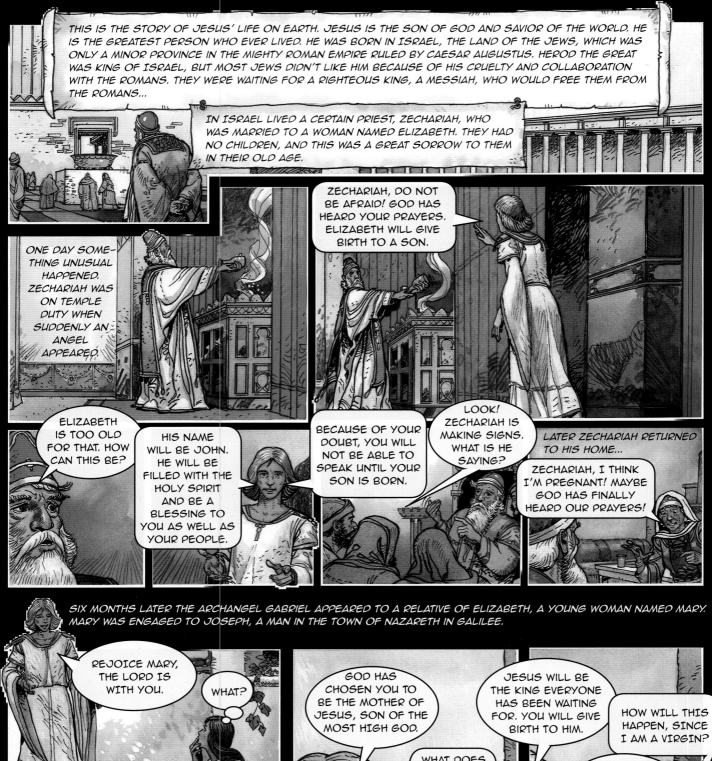

ONE MORE THING. YOUR RELATIVE ELIZABETH IS ALSO HAVING A SON. SHE IS ALREADY SIX MONTHS PREGNANT.

MARY KNEW THAT ANY WOMAN WHO WAS PREGNANT OUTSIDE OF MARRIAGE WOULD BE IN SERIOUS TROUBLE. WHAT WOULD HER FIANCÉ, JOSEPH, SAY WHEN SHE TOLD HIM SHE WAS WITH CHILD? STILL, SHE CHOSE TO TRUST GOD.

MAY IT HAPPEN ACCORDING TO YOUR WORD.

THEN THE ANGEL DISAPPEARED.

ELIZABETH WOULD UNDERSTAND! MARY COULD HARDLY WAIT TO TELL HER THE NEWS. SHE RODE ALL THE WAY FROM NAZARETH TO ELIZABETH'S HOME IN JUDEA.

MARY!

ELIZABETH!

THE BABY IN MY WOMB LEAPED FOR JOY AT THE SOUND OF YOUR VOICE!

MARY THEN PRAISED GOD FOR ALL HE HAD DONE.

MY SOUL PRAISES THE GREATNESS OF THE LORD! MY SPIRIT RE-JOICES IN MY SAVING GOD!

DANCE, MARY, DANCE! THE LORD HAS BEEN GOOD TO BOTH OF US.

MARY STAYED WITH ELIZA-BETH FOR THREE MONTHS.

ELIZABETH GAVE BIRTH TO A HEALTHY BOY. ALL HER NEIGHBORS AND RELATIVES REJOICED WITH HER. WHEN THE BOY WAS 8 DAYS OLD, HE WAS TO BE CIRCUMCISED AND NAMED.

HE SHOULD BE NAMED AFTER HIS FATHER, ZECHARIAH!

WHAT DOES HIS FATHER THINK?

I THINK HE SHOULD BE CALLED JOHN.

ZECHARIAH WROTE ON A TABLET: HIS NAME IS JOHN!

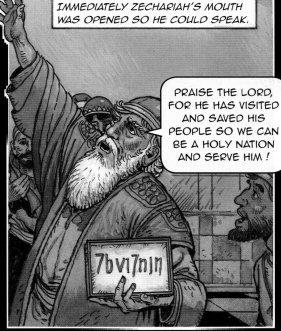

IMMEDIATELY ZECHARIAH'S MOUTH WAS OPENED SO HE COULD SPEAK.

PRAISE THE LORD, FOR HE HAS VISITED AND SAVED HIS PEOPLE SO WE CAN BE A HOLY NATION AND SERVE HIM!

JOHN GREW UP TO BECOME A MAN OF SPIRITUAL STRENGTH. HE LIVED IN THE DESERT UNTIL THE DAY HE APPEAREDP PUBLICLY TO THE PEOPLE OF ISRAEL.

THEN THE HAPPY PARENTS-TO-BE WERE MARRIED.

MONTHS WENT BY. LIFE IN THE SMALL TOWN OF NAZARETH WENT ON AS USUAL. JOSEPH WAS BUSY IN HIS WORKSHOP, AND MARY WAS COUNTING THE DAYS UNTIL SHE WOULD GIVE BIRTH. THEN ONE DAY A ROMAN OFFICIAL ARRIVED IN TOWN...

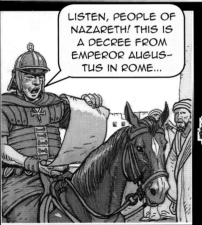

LISTEN, PEOPLE OF NAZARETH! THIS IS A DECREE FROM EMPEROR AUGUSTUS IN ROME...

CEASAR WANTS TO COUNT ALL THE PEOPLE IN HIS EMPIRE. THE DESCENDENTS OF KING DAVID WILL HAVE TO GO TO BETHLEHEM IN JUDEA TO BE REGISTERED.

THIS IS A LONG TRIP, MARY. THINK YOU CAN MAKE IT?

SOON THEY WERE ON THEIR WAY...

MANY OTHER TRAVELERS WERE ALSO ON THEIR WAY TO BETHLEHEM.

LOOK, JERUSALEM! BETHLEHEM CAN'T BE FAR AWAY.

AT LAST THEY ARRIVED IN BETHLEHEM. BUT THE NIGHT WAS COLD, AND THEY NEEDED A PLACE TO SLEEP.

JOSEPH, I THINK IT'S TIME FOR THE BABY TO BE BORN.

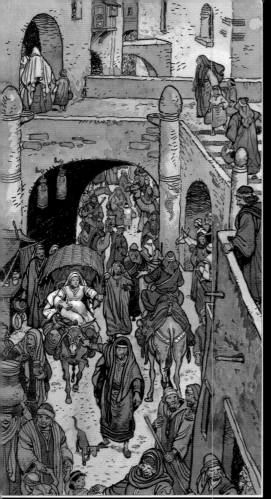

THERE WERE MANY PEOPLE IN TOWN. JOSEPH WENT FROM PLACE TO PLACE...

SORRY, NO VACANCY.

MARY WAS IN LABOR, AND JOSEPH WAS GETTING DESPERATE...

I KNOW SOMEONE WHO MIGHT BE ABLE TO HELP YOU.

OK, YOU MAY STAY IN MY STABLE FOR THE NIGHT.

THIS WAY!

JOSEPH, IT'S TIME!

MAY GOD HELP YOU!

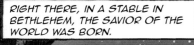

RIGHT THERE, IN A STABLE IN BETHLEHEM, THE SAVIOR OF THE WORLD WAS BORN.

MARY AND JOSEPH LOOKED AT THE BABY AND WERE AMAZED THAT THEY WERE HOLDING THE MESSIAH, THE SON OF GOD, IN THEIR ARMS. MARY WONDERED WHAT HIS LIFE WOULD BE LIKE. HOW WOULD HE SAVE THEIR PEOPLE AND BRING LIGHT TO THE WORLD?

IN THE FIELDS NEAR BETHLEHEM SOME SHEPHERDS WERE WATCHING THEIR SHEEP WHEN AN ANGEL APPEARED...

WHEN JESUS HAD BEEN CIRCUMCISED AND NAMED, JOSEPH AND MARY TOOK HIM TO THE TEMPLE IN JERUSALEM TO MAKE A SPECIAL OFFERING TO GOD--A PAIR OF TURTLEDOVES OR TWO YOUNG PIGEONS.

HIS NAME IS JESUS, WHICH MEANS 'GOD SAVES.'

MARY WILL SUFFER GREAT PAIN. FOR ALTHOUGH MANY WILL REJOICE BECAUSE OF HIM, OTHERS WILL HATE HIM WHEN HE REVEALS THEIR INNER-MOST THOUGHTS.

AN OLD MAN OF GOD NAMED SIMEON CAME UP TO MARY AND JOSEPH...

CAN I HOLD HIM? GOD TOLD ME I WOULD LIVE TO SEE THE SAVIOR.

GOD, NOW LET YOUR SERVANT DIE IN PEACE FOR I HAVE SEEN THE SAVIOR WITH MY OWN EYES.

THIS CHILD WILL BE A LIGHT TO THE PEOPLE OF ISRAEL AND ALL THE WORLD!

IN THE TEMPLE WAS ALSO AN OLD WOMAN NAMED ANNA. SHE NEVER LEFT THE TEMPLE. SHE FASTED AND PRAYED DAY AND NIGHT, AND SHE ALWAYS TALKED TO PEOPLE ABOUT THE COMING SAVIOR.

THIS CHILD WILL RESCUE JERUSALEM!

JESUS PRESENTED IN THE TEMPLE Luke 2:21–38

FAR AWAY IN THE EAST LIVED THREE WISE MEN CALLED MAGI. IN THE SKY, THEY NOTICED AN UNUSUALLY BRIGHT STAR. THEY KNEW THE STAR SIGNIFIED AN IMPORTANT EVENT, SO THEY FOLLOWED THE STAR AND FINALLY ARRIVED IN JERUSALEM.

WE HAVE SEEN THE STAR OF THE FUTURE KING OF THE JEWS. WHERE CAN WE FIND HIM?

WHEN HEROD HEARD ABOUT A NEW KING, HE GOT UPSET AND SUMMONED THE CHIEF PRIESTS AND WISE MEN TO HIS COURT. HE ASKED THEM WHERE THE SCRIPTURES SAID THIS KING WOULD BE BORN. THEY TOLD HIM:

THE MESSIAH WILL BE BORN IN BETHLEHEM!

"OUT OF YOU, BETHLEHEM IN JUDEA, WILL COME A RULER AND SHEPHERD OF MY PEOPLE ISRAEL!" (MICAH 5:2)
NOW HEROD WAS REALLY WORRIED. HE CALLED THE MAGI...

WHEN YOU FIND THIS KING, LET ME KNOW WHERE HE IS. I WANT TO WORSHIP HIM TOO!

THIS WAS A LIE. HEROD HAD OTHER PLANS.

I MUST KILL HIM.

THE MAGI LEFT AND CAME TO THE PLACE WHERE THE BABY WAS...

...AND THEY WORSHIPED HIM AND OFFERED HIM EXPENSIVE GIFTS OF GOLD, FRANKINCENSE, AND MYRRH. THEN THEY RETURNED TO THEIR COUNTRY WITHOUT TELLING HEROD WHERE THEY HAD FOUND HIM..

MARY, I'M SURE GOD WILL PROTECT US.

THAT NIGHT JOSEPH HAD A DREAM. IN THE DREAM AN ANGEL SAID TO HIM:

JOSEPH, WAKE UP! HEROD WANTS TO KILL THE CHILD. YOU MUST FLEE TO EGYPT.

MARY, GET UP! THE ANGEL TOLD US TO LEAVE.

WHEN THE SUN CAME UP, THEY WERE ON THEIR WAY TO EGYPT.

WHEN HEROD REALIZED HE HAD BEEN OUT-WITTED BY THE MAGI, HE WAS FURIOUS.

GO HOUSE TO HOUSE IN BETHLEHEM AND KILL EVERY BOY UNDER TWO YEARS OF AGE!

THE SOLDIERS CARRIED OUT THE KING'S ORDERS...

SIR, EVERY BOY UNDER TWO IS DEAD.

IN THE MEANTIME JESUS AND HIS PARENTS HAD ARRIVED SAFELY IN EGYPT.

THEY STAYED THERE FAR FROM HOME...

...UNTIL THE ANGEL TOLD THEM IT WAS SAFE TO RETURN.

I REALLY LOOK FOR-WARD TO BEING HOME.

HEROD DIED AND WAS SUCCEEDED BY HIS SON WHO WAS EVEN WORSE THAN HIS FATHER.

I AM THE GREATEST KING EVER IN ISRAEL. WRITE IT DOWN!

AFTER THEIR LONG JOURNEY...

WELCOME HOME!

BACK IN NAZARETH, NOT FAR FROM THE KING'S PALACE, JOSEPH, MARY, AND JESUS WERE RECEIVED WITH JOY.

JESUS GREW AND HELPED JOSEPH IN HIS CAR-PENTRY WORKSHOP. HE WAS GROWING UP TO BE-COME A MATURE YOUNG MAN, FULL OF WISDOM AND PLEASANT TO BE WITH.

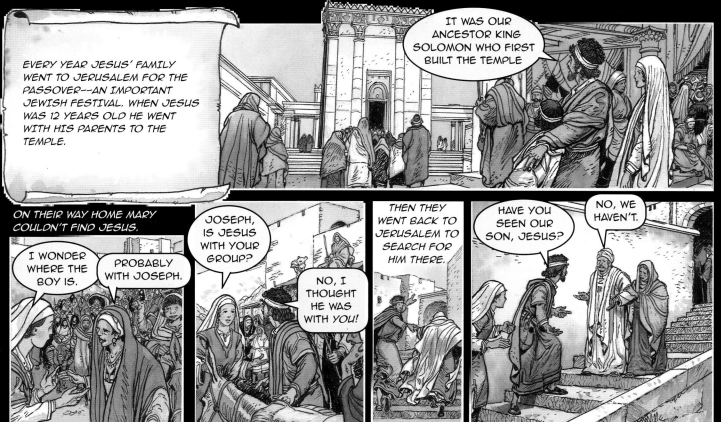

EVERY YEAR JESUS' FAMILY WENT TO JERUSALEM FOR THE PASSOVER--AN IMPORTANT JEWISH FESTIVAL. WHEN JESUS WAS 12 YEARS OLD HE WENT WITH HIS PARENTS TO THE TEMPLE.

IT WAS OUR ANCESTOR KING SOLOMON WHO FIRST BUILT THE TEMPLE

ON THEIR WAY HOME MARY COULDN'T FIND JESUS.

I WONDER WHERE THE BOY IS.

PROBABLY WITH JOSEPH.

JOSEPH, IS JESUS WITH YOUR GROUP?

NO, I THOUGHT HE WAS WITH YOU!

THEN THEY WENT BACK TO JERUSALEM TO SEARCH FOR HIM THERE.

HAVE YOU SEEN OUR SON, JESUS?

NO, WE HAVEN'T.

FOR THREE DAYS THEY WERE SEARCHING FOR JESUS.

WE'VE LOOKED ALL OVER TOWN!

THERE HE IS--INSIDE THE TEMPLE!

HE'S TALKING WITH THE RELIGIOUS TEACHERS!

WE'VE LOOKED ALL OVER FOR YOU! WHY DID YOU DO THIS TO US?

YOU DIDN'T NEED TO LOOK FOR ME. YOU SHOULD HAVE KNOWN I MUST BE IN MY FATHER'S HOUSE.

AT THAT TIME THEY DIDN'T KNOW WHAT JESUS MEANT. BUT MARY STORED ALL THESE THINGS IN HER HEART. AFTER THIS JESUS RETURNED WITH THEM TO NAZARETH, AND HE CONTINUED TO GROW IN WISDOM. GOD WAS PLEASED WITH HIM, AND SO WERE THE PEOPLE AROUND HIM.

IN MY FATHER'S HOUSE Luke 2:41–52

THE BAPTISM OF JESUS Luke 3:1–22; Matthew 3:13–17; Mark 1:10–11; John 1:19–34

Ministry

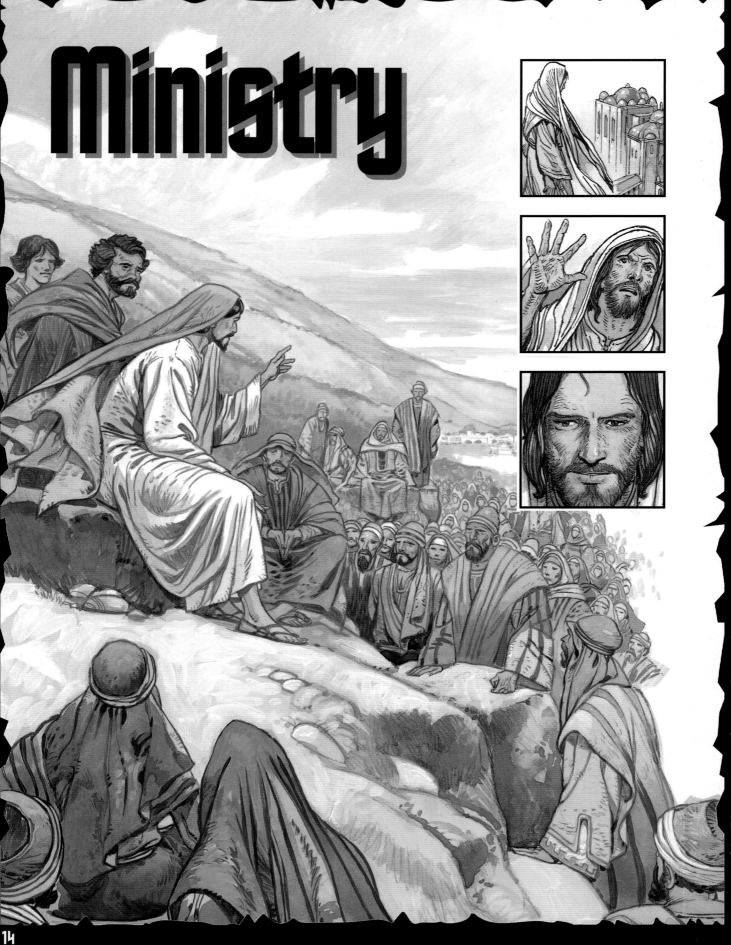

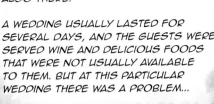

SOON AFTERWARD, JESUS AND HIS DISCIPLES WERE INVITED TO A WEDDING. JESUS' MOTHER, MARY, WAS ALSO THERE.

A WEDDING USUALLY LASTED FOR SEVERAL DAYS, AND THE GUESTS WERE SERVED WINE AND DELICIOUS FOODS THAT WERE NOT USUALLY AVAILABLE TO THEM. BUT AT THIS PARTICULAR WEDDING THERE WAS A PROBLEM...

WE'RE OUT OF WINE!

THERE'S NO MORE WINE. MAYBE IT'S TIME FOR JESUS TO STEP IN.

SON, THEY ARE OUT OF WINE.

MAYBE YOU CAN HELP THEM.

WHY ARE YOU TELLING ME THIS? MY TIME HAS NOT YET COME.

MARY WENT TO THE SERVANTS...

DO WHATEVER HE TELLS YOU.

FILL THE JARS WITH WATER.

DIP SOME OUT AND TAKE IT TO THE MASTER OF CEREMONIES.

THE MASTER OF CEREMONIES HAD NO IDEA WHERE THE WINE CAME FROM.

THIS IS A GOOD WINE-- VERY GOOD!

THE MASTER OF CEREMONIES WENT TO THE BRIDEGROOM...

WHY DID YOU SAVE THE BEST WINE UNTIL NOW?

THIS WAS THE FIRST PUBLIC MIRACLE JESUS DID--TURNING WATER INTO WINE AT A WEDDING IN THE TOWN OF CANA IN GALILEE.

MERCHANTS IN THE TEMPLE John 2:12–25

NICODEMUS, LISTEN! UNLESS YOU'RE BORN AGAIN, YOU CAN'T SEE THE KINGDOM OF GOD.

WHAT DO YOU MEAN? NO ONE CAN GO BACK INTO THEIR MOTHER'S WOMB.

NO, YOU MUST BE BORN FROM ABOVE --BY WATER AND THE SPIRIT OF GOD.

HOW IS THIS POSSIBLE?

THROUGH FAITH.

"GOD LOVED THE WORLD SO MUCH THAT HE GAVE HIS OWN SON, SO THAT EVERYONE WHO BE-LIEVES IN HIM MAY NOT BE LOST BUT INSTEAD MAY HAVE EVERLASTING LIFE." (JOHN 3:16)

I AM A TEACHER IN ISRAEL, BUT I HAVE NO IDEA WHAT HE MEANS.

RUMORS ABOUT JESUS GOT AROUND. MORE AND MORE PEOPLE WANTED TO SEE HIM. THIS MADE THE RELIGIOUS LEADERS FURIOUS FOR THEY FEARED HE MIGHT CAUSE EVEN MORE TROUBLE THAN JOHN THE BAPTIST. THEY WERE RELIEVED WHEN JESUS FINALLY LEFT JUDEA AND HEADED NORTH TOWARD GALILEE.

JESUS, THIS ROAD WILL TAKE US THROUGH SAMARIA. DON'T WE WANT TO AVOID THE SAMARITANS?

AT MIDDAY THEY STOPPED AT JACOB'S WELL.

LET'S TAKE A REST.

WE'LL GO TO TOWN AND BUY SOME FOOD.

WHILE JESUS WAS WAITING FOR THEM, A WOMAN CAME OUT TO DRAW WATER FROM THE WELL.

PLEASE GIVE ME A DRINK!

A JEWISH MAN ISN'T SUPPOSED TO TALK TO A SAMARITAN WOMAN.

YOU DON'T KNOW WHO I AM, AND YOU HAVE NO IDEA WHAT GOD CAN GIVE. IF YOU WOULD ASK ME, I WOULD GIVE YOU LIVING WATER.

BUT YOU HAVE NOTHING TO DRAW WATER WITH. BESIDES, ARE YOU GREATER THAN OUR ANCESTOR JACOB WHO BUILT THIS WELL?

DRINK THIS WATER AND YOU WILL THIRST AGAIN. THE WATER I GIVE WILL BE LIKE A SPRING INSIDE YOU.

SIR, PLEASE GIVE ME THAT WATER! THEN I'LL NEVER BE THIRSTY AGAIN.

GO GET YOUR HUSBAND!

I DON'T HAVE ONE.

TRUE, YOU HAVE HAD FIVE, AND THE ONE YOU LIVE WITH NOW IS NOT YOUR HUSBAND.

SIR, YOU MUST BE A PROPHET! TELL ME WHERE TO WORSHIP GOD--ON THIS HOLY MOUNTAIN OR ONLY IN THE TEMPLE IN JERUSALEM?

THE TIME HAS COME WHEN IT DOESN'T MATTER WHERE YOU WORSHIP GOD...

THEN SHE GOT UP AND SERVED THEM.

THAT EVENING MANY PEOPLE BROUGHT THEIR SICK FRIENDS AND RELATIVES TO JESUS. HE LAID HANDS ON THEM, AND THEY WERE HEALED. OTHERS WERE DELIVERED FROM EVIL SPIRITS.

AT DAYBREAK JESUS WENT TO A SOLITARY PLACE TO PRAY.

FATHER, I AM ONE WITH YOU.

ON HIS WAY BACK, HE MET SIMON...

WHERE HAVE YOU BEEN? THE PEOPLE HAVE MANY NEEDS. THEY WANT YOU TO STAY HERE.

I MUST PREACH GOD'S KINGDOM IN OTHER TOWNS AS WELL.

IN ANOTHER TOWN THEY MET A MAN WITH LEPROSY...

WATCH OUT, HE'S UNCLEAN! GET OUT OF HERE!

DON'T LET HIM GET NEAR JESUS!

MASTER, IF YOU WANT TO, YOU CAN HEAL ME!

I DO WANT TO. BE HEALED!

IMMEDIATELY THE LEPROSY WENT AWAY.

LOOK! MY HANDS!

DON'T TALK ABOUT THIS. INSTEAD GO TO THE PRIEST AND LET HIM WITNESS YOUR HEALING.

THEN OFFER THANKS TO GOD IN THE TEMPLE.

BUT THE MAN WAS TOO [...] EXCITED TO KEEP QUIET...

I'M HEALED! JESUS HEALED ME!

SO THE NEWS ABOUT JESUS SPREAD, AND PEOPLE CAME TO SEE HIM. BUT JESUS WENT AWAY TO PRAY.

A FEW DAYS LATER, JESUS RETURNED TO CAPERNAUM WHERE HE WAS INVITED TO SOMEONE'S HOUSE. WHEN THE PEOPLE HEARD THAT JESUS WAS BACK IN TOWN, THEY RAN TO THE HOUSE TO LISTEN TO JESUS. FOUR FRIENDS OF A LAME MAN WANTED JESUS TO HEAL THEIR FRIEND.

WELCOME, MASTER!

HEY, WE CAN'T POSSIBLY GET OUR FRIEND INSIDE.

I HAVE AN IDEA.

WE'LL MAKE A HOLE IN THE ROOF!

GREAT IDEA!

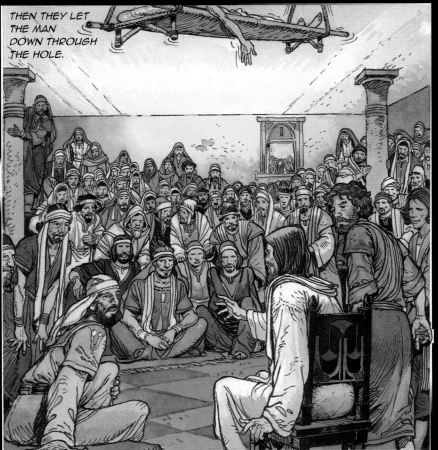

THEN THEY LET THE MAN DOWN THROUGH THE HOLE.

MASTER, PLEASE HEAL OUR FRIEND!

ANYONE WHO PUTS MY TEACHING INTO PRACTICE IS LIKE A WISE MAN WHO BUILT HIS HOUSE ON ROCK. THE RAIN CAME, AND THE WINDS BEAT AGAINST IT, BUT IT DIDN'T COLLAPSE.

ANYONE WHO DOESN'T PUT MY TEACHING INTO PRACTICE IS LIKE A FOOLISH MAN WHO BUILT HIS HOUSE ON SAND. WHEN THE RAIN CAME, AND THE WINDS BEAT AGAINST THAT HOUSE, IT COLLAPSED WITH A GREAT CRASH.

THE CROWDS WERE AMAZED AT JESUS' TEACHING. HE SPOKE WITH AUTHORITY--NOT LIKE THE OTHER RELIGIOUS TEACHERS IN ISRAEL.

WHEN JESUS HAD FINISHED SPEAKING, HE WENT TO CAPERNAUM...

SIR, PLEASE COME WITH US. A ROMAN CENTURION ASKS YOU TO HEAL HIS SERVANT WHO IS SICK.

WHY?

HE VALUES HIS SERVANT HIGHLY AND DOESN'T WANT HIM TO DIE.

BUT WHY ARE YOU COMING ON HIS BEHALF?

HE DOESN'T FEEL WORTHY TO COME TO YOU. BESIDES, HE LOVES OUR PEOPLE. HE HELPED BUILD OUR SYNAGOGUE.

OK, I'LL GO WITH YOU.

IN THE MEANTIME THE ROMAN CENTURION HAD SECOND THOUGHTS.

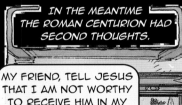

MY FRIEND, TELL JESUS THAT I AM NOT WORTHY TO RECEIVE HIM IN MY HOUSE.

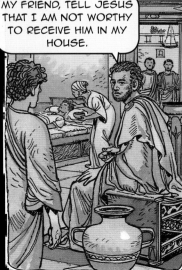

HE BELIEVES YOU CAN HEAL HIS SERVANT EVEN WITH-OUT SEEING HIM.

HE THINKS A WORD FROM YOU IS ENOUGH.

I KNOW ABOUT THE CHAIN OF COM-MAND. TELL JESUS I BELIEVE HE CAN COMMAND EVIL AND SICKNESS THE SAME WAY I CAN COMMAND MY SOLDIERS.

WHEN THEY TOLD JESUS ABOUT THE CENTURION'S FAITH, JESUS WAS AMAZED.

A SOLDIER'S FAITH Luke 7:1-10; 11-17

31

NEVER HAVE I FOUND SUCH TRUST AMONG OUR OWN PEOPLE. HE WILL BE HEALED.

WHEN THE MEN RETURNED TO THE CAPTAIN, THEY FOUND THE SERVANT UP AND WELL.

MOST PEOPLE IN ISRAEL DIDN'T KNOW WHAT TO MAKE OF JESUS. THEY COULDN'T DENY HIS HEALINGS AND MIRACLES, BUT IT WAS DIFFICULT FOR MOST OF THEM TO UNDERSTAND HIS TEACHING AND BELIEVE HE WAS THE MESSIAH PROMISED BY THE OLD PROPHETS. MAYBE HE WAS JUST A PROPHET TOO, OR COULD HE ACTUALLY BE THE SON OF GOD?

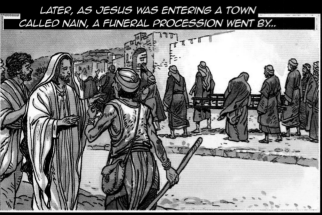

LATER, AS JESUS WAS ENTERING A TOWN CALLED NAIN, A FUNERAL PROCESSION WENT BY...

THE DEAD PERSON WAS A WIDOW'S ONLY SON.

WOMAN, DON'T CRY!

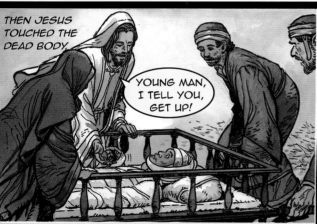

THEN JESUS TOUCHED THE DEAD BODY.

YOUNG MAN, I TELL YOU, GET UP!

IMMEDIATELY HE SAT UP AND BEGAN TALKING.

YOUR SON IS BACK.

WHAT A PROPHET! GOD IS AMONG HIS PEOPLE. HE CARES FOR US!

THE GOOD NEWS OF JESUS WAS SPREADING LIKE WILDFIRE ACROSS GALILEE AND BEYOND.

Miracles

ONE DAY A PHARISEE NAMED SIMON INVITED JESUS TO DINNER AT HIS HOUSE. A SINFUL WOMAN WANTED TO MEET JESUS, SO DURING THE DINNER SHE WALKED INTO SIMON'S HOUSE. THIS WAS AN AWKWARD SITUATION BECAUSE PHARISEES WERE DIGNIFIED RELIGIOUS LEADERS WHO DESPISED AND AVOIDED SINNERS

THE WOMAN KNELT BEFORE JESUS AND WEPT.

HOW DISGRACEFUL! DOESN'T JESUS KNOW WHAT KIND OF WOMAN SHE IS?

LOOK! SHE'S WIPING HIS FEET WITH HER HAIR.

THE WOMAN EVEN KISSED HIS FEET.

THIS IS ALL WRONG. JESUS CAN'T POSSIBLY BE A MAN OF GOD.

SIMON, I HAVE SOMETHING TO SAY TO YOU.

YES, TEACHER!

A MAN LOANED MONEY TO TWO PEOPLE —$5,000 TO ONE AND $50,000 TO THE OTHER. NEITHER OF THEM COULD PAY HIM BACK, SO HE CANCELED THEIR DEBTS.

NOW WHICH OF THEM WILL LOVE HIM MORE?

THE ONE WHO OWED HIM THE MOST, I GUESS.

RIGHT! NOW LOOK AT THIS WOMAN. WHEN I ENTERED YOUR HOUSE, YOU DIDN'T BOTHER TO OFFER ME WATER TO WASH MY FEET...

...BUT SHE WET MY FEET WITH HER TEARS AND WIPED THEM WITH HER HAIR.

SHE EVEN KISSED 'M AND POURED PERFUME ON THEM.

SHE LOVES MUCH. THEREFORE HER MANY SINS HAVE BEEN FORGIVEN.

BUT ONLY GOD CAN FORGIVE SINS!

IS HE THE MESSIAH WE'VE BEEN WAITING FOR?

FAITH HAS SAVED YOU. GO IN PEACE!

WHO IS HE? I SAW HIM HEAL A MAN WHO WAS POSSESSED BY THOUSANDS OF DEMONS!

"THE MAN WAS SO VIOLENT THAT NO ONE COULD CONTROL HIM. BUT JESUS SIMPLY COMMANDED THE DEMONS TO LEAVE HIM."

"AFTERWARD TH MAN WAS COMPLETELY CALM

I BET HE'S DRIVING OUT DEMONS BY THE POWER OF THE PRINCE OF DEMONS.

HE HASN'T PROVED YET THAT HIS TEACHINGS AND MIRACLES ARE FROM GOD.

I KNOW WHAT YOU'RE THINKING. BUT WOULDN'T YOU AGREE THAT A KINGDOM THAT IS AT WAR WITH ITSELF IS DOOMED TO FAIL?

THEN WHY THIS NONSENSE? WHY CAN'T YOU JUST ACCEPT THAT GOD IS AT WORK HERE AND HIS KINGDOM HAS COME?

LISTEN! ANYONE WHO IS NOT WITH ME IS AGAINST ME. AND ANYONE WHO DOESN'T WORK WITH ME IS WORKING AGAINST ME.

JEWS HAD RITUALS FOR CLEANSING BEFORE EATING.

ONE DAY, JESUS WAS INVITED TO THE HOME OF A PHARISEE WHO QUESTIONED JESUS' OBSERVANCE OF THESE RITUALS.

JESUS RECLINED AT THE TABLE.

JESUS, YOU HAVEN'T DONE ALL THE RITUAL CLEANING.

PEOPLE! YOU CLEAN EVERYTHING ON THE OUTSIDE, BUT YOU DON'T CARE ABOUT THE INSIDE.

YOU'RE NOT ONLY CRITICIZING THE PHARISEES BUT YOU'RE INSULTING US, JESUS!

SO BE IT.

WOE TO YOU, EXPERTS OF THE LAW! YOU HAVE GAINED MUCH KNOWLEDGE ABOUT GOD...

...BUT YOU MAKE YOUR KNOWLEDGE AN OBSTACLE FOR OTHERS WHO WANT TO GET TO KNOW GOD.

SUDDENLY A MAN CAME UP TO JESUS...

TEACHER, OUR FATHER JUST DIED. PLEASE TELL MY BROTHER TO SHARE THE INHERITANCE WITH ME AS THE LAW PRESCRIBES.

I'M NOT HERE TO MEDIATE BETWEEN YOU AND YOUR BROTHER.

BUT I TELL YOU, BEWARE OF GREED! HAPPINESS ISN'T FOUND IN THE THINGS YOU OWN.

THEN JESUS TOLD THEM A STORY:

THERE WAS A WEALTHY FARMER WHO HAD MUCH LAND AND RICH HARVESTS. "I'LL TEAR DOWN MY OLD BARNS AND BUILD BIGGER ONES TO STORE MY CROPS," HE THOUGHT.

...BUT YOU MAKE YOUR

"THEN I'LL RETIRE AND TELL MYSELF TO TAKE IT EASY. I'LL EAT, DRINK, AND BE HAPPY."

BUT GOD SAID TO THE MAN, "YOU FOOL! TONIGHT YOU WILL DIE. THEN WHAT WILL BECOME OF ALL THIS YOU HAVE STORED UP?"

THIS IS WHAT WILL HAPPEN TO THOSE WHO STORE UP RICHES FOR THEMSELVES. IN GOD'S EYES THEY'RE NOT WEALTHY AT ALL.

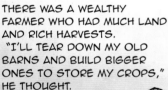

AFTER THIS THE PHARISEES AND THE TEACHERS OF THE LAW BEGAN TO LOOK FOR WAYS TO CATCH JESUS OFF GUARD.

HERE'S ANOTHER PARABLE JESUS TOLD:

A MAN FOUND A TREASURE IN A FIELD...

I MUST HIDE THIS TREASURE AND BUY THE WHOLE FIELD. THEN THE TREASURE WILL BE MINE.

SO THE MAN SOLD EVERYTHING HE OWNED AND BOUGHT THE FIELD.

YOU SEE, WHEN YOU FIND THE TREASURE, YOU WILL SACRIFICE EVERYTHING ELSE IN ORDER TO HAVE IT.

THE DISCIPLES BEGAN TO REALIZE THE COST OF FOLLOWING JESUS AND HIS WORD. SOME LEFT HIM BECAUSE THEY FELT THE PRICE WAS TOO HIGH; OTHERS WANTED MORE:

GOD'S KINGDOM IS LIKE A TINY MUSTARD SEED THAT A MAN PLANTED IN HIS GARDEN.

THE SEED SPROUTED AND GREW INTO A TALL TREE WHERE THE BIRDS COULD BUILD NESTS AND HATCH THEIR YOUNG.

JESUS WANT-ED TO SHOW THEM HOW THE KINGDOM OF GOD MAY SEEM SMALL...

...AND INSIGNIFICANT AT FIR BUT LATER IT WILL GROW IN SOMETHING REALLY BIG.

JESUS TOLD THEM ANOTHER STORY: THE KINGDOM OF GOD IS LIKE A FISHING NET CAST NTO THE SEA. IN THE CATCH WERE BOTH GOOD FISH AND WORTHLESS FISH.

THE FISHERMEN THREW AWAY THE BAD FISH AND KEPT THE GOOD FISH.

THIS IS WHAT WILL HAPPEN AT THE OF TIME. GOD'S ANGEL SEPARATE THE PEOPL LOVE GOD FROM TH WHO HAVE CHOSEN REJECT HIM.

MOST OF THE TIME, JESUS WAS SURROUNDED BY PEOPLE WITH MANY DIFFERENT NEEDS. ONE DAY HE TOLD THE DISCIPLES TO GET INTO THEIR BOATS.

SIMON, LET'S GO TO THE OTHER SHORE.

MASTER, TAKE A REST. WE'LL DO THE WORK.

JESUS LAY DOWN TO REST.

WE'LL WAKE YOU UP WHEN WE GET THERE.

BUT A BIG STORM BLEW ACROSS THE LAKE. THE DISCIPLES WERE SCARED.

MASTER, WAKE UP! WE'RE DROWNING!

OTHER SIDE OF THE LAKE. WHEN JESUS AND THE DISCIPLES GOT THERE, A MAN WHO WAS POSSESSED BY DEMONS MET THEM.

WHAT IS YOUR NAME?

MY NAME IS LEGION BECAUSE THERE ARE MANY DEMONS IN ME.

WHY DO YOU TORTURE US? LEAVE US ALONE!

YOU EVIL SPIRITS, COME OUT OF THIS MAN!

NO, PLEASE DON'T CAST US OUT!

AT LEAST SEND US INTO THE PIGS OVER THERE!

GO!

THERE WERE ABOUT 2,000 PIGS IN THE HERD. WHEN THE EVIL SPIRITS LEFT THE MAN, THEY WENT INTO THE PIGS. THE PIGS RAN OFF THE EDGE OF A CLIFF AND DROWNED.

THE SWINEHERD PANICKED AND RAN BACK TO THE VILLAGE TO TELL THE PEOPLE WHAT HAD HAPPENED.

THE HERD HAS DROWNED!

THEN THE WHOLE VILLAGE RAN OUT TO SEE THE MAN WHO HAD CAUSED THIS.

BESIDES, HE CONSIDERED JOHN A GOOD AND HOLY MAN, AND HE LIKED TO VISIT HIM IN PRISON AND HEAR HIM TEACH.

ONE DAY THE OPPORTUNITY HERODIAS HAD BEEN WAITING FOR CAME. ON HIS BIRTHDAY HEROD GAVE A DINNER PARTY FOR HIS TOP OFFICIALS, MILITARY COMMANDERS, AND OTHER IMPORTANT LEADERS.

DURING THE PARTY HERODIAS' DAUGHTER, SALOME, DANCED FOR THE KING AND HIS GUESTS. THEY WERE VERY PLEASED WITH HER. HEROD WANTED TO IMPRESS HIS GUESTS. SOON, HOWEVER, HE WOULD REGRET HIS DECISION....

WHEN SALOME HAD FINISHED HER DANCE, THE KING CALLED FOR HER...

WONDERFUL! WHAT CAN I GIVE YOU IN RETURN?

I'LL GIVE YOU ANYTHING YOU WANT. WHATEVER YOU ASK FOR I'LL GIVE YOU-- EVEN HALF MY KINGDOM.

THIS WAS THE MOMENT HERODIAS HAD BEEN WAITING FOR.

MOTHER, WHAT SHOULD I ASK FOR?

GO BACK AND TELL HEROD THIS...

...JOHN THE BAPTIST'S HEAD ON THIS SILVER PLATE!

HEROD WAS SHOCKED, BUT HE COULDN'T BREAK THE PROMISE HE HAD MADE IN FRONT OF HIS GUESTS.

GIVE HER WHAT SHE ASKS FOR.

IN PRISON JOHN WAS WONDERING WHETHER HE HAD FULFILLED HIS MISSION. THEN HE REMEMBERED HIS WORDS TO HIS DISCIPLES...

JESUS MUST BECOME GREATER, AND I MUST BECOME LESS.

JOHN WAS READY TO DIE. THE SOLDIER LIFTED HIS SWORD, AND WITH ONE STRIKE...

SLAM!

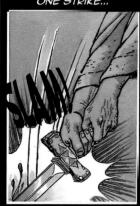

MOMENTS LATER, JOHN'S HEAD WAS GIVEN TO SALOME ON THE SILVER PLATE.

THE GIRL BROUGHT IT TO HERODIAS.

FINALLY DEAD!

LATER, JOHN'S DISCIPLES CAME AND TOOK JOHN'S BODY AND BURIED IT IN A TOMB.

WHEN JESUS HEARD WHAT HAD HAPPENED TO HIS DEAR COUSIN, HE LEFT IN A BOAT. HE WANTED TO BE ALONE AND REMEMBER JOHN, BUT HE ALSO WANTED TO SEEK GOD'S WILL FOR HIS OWN MISSION AND DESTINY.

KING HEROD ANTIPAS WHOM JESUS WOULD LATER CALL "THAT FOX," RULED AS KING OF THE NORTHERN TERRITORY FOR ANOTHER EIGHT YEARS. HE SUFFERED A HORRIBLE DEATH--JUST LIKE HIS FATHER HEROD THE GREAT WHO HAD CONSIDERED HIMSELF A GOD AND HAD BRUTALLY KILLED ALL THE LITTLE BOYS IN BETHLEHEM SHORTLY AFTER JESUS WAS BORN.

Teachings

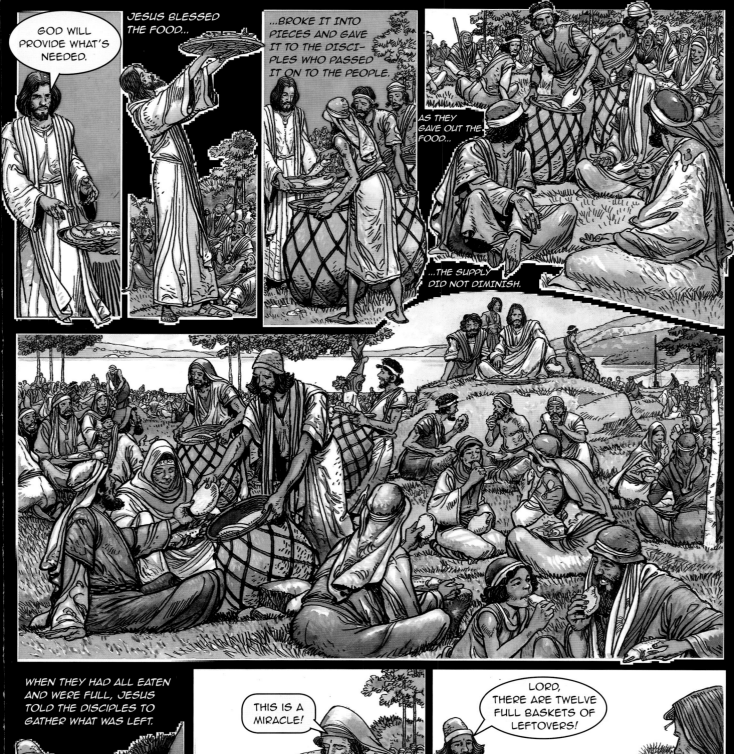

GOD WILL PROVIDE WHAT'S NEEDED.

JESUS BLESSED THE FOOD...

...BROKE IT INTO PIECES AND GAVE IT TO THE DISCIPLES WHO PASSED IT ON TO THE PEOPLE.

AS THEY GAVE OUT THE FOOD...

...THE SUPPLY DID NOT DIMINISH.

WHEN THEY HAD ALL EATEN AND WERE FULL, JESUS TOLD THE DISCIPLES TO GATHER WHAT WAS LEFT.

THIS IS A MIRACLE!

LORD, THERE ARE TWELVE FULL BASKETS OF LEFTOVERS!

51

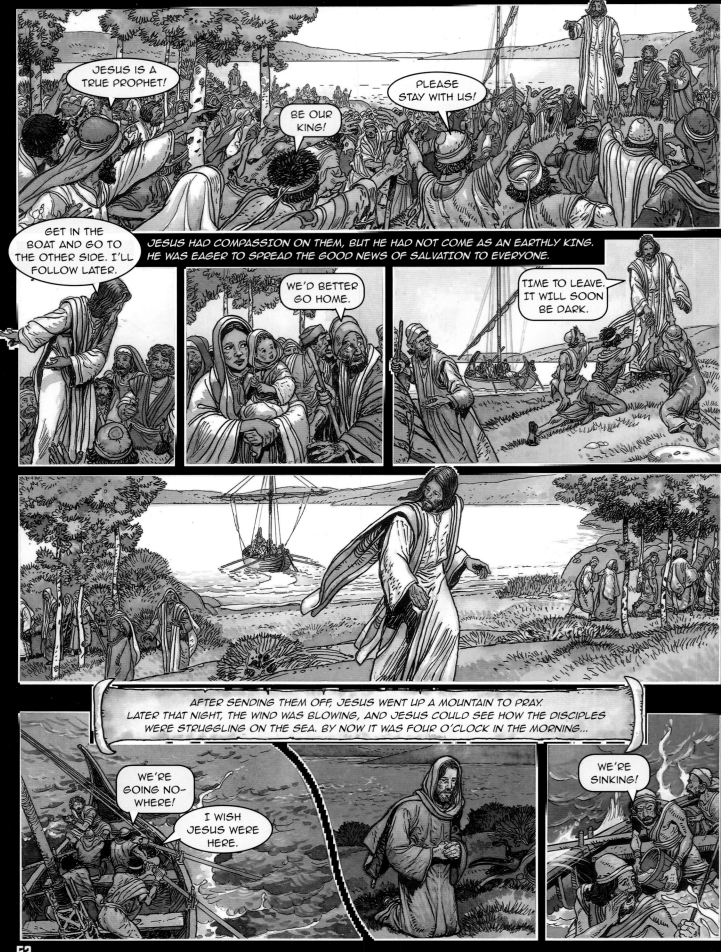

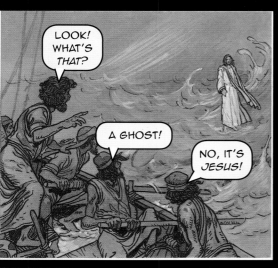

AS SOON AS JESUS AND PETER GOT INTO THE BOAT, THE WIND DIED DOWN, AND THE SEA GREW CALM.

EARLY IN THE MORNING, THEY LANDED AT GENNESARET ON THE SHORE OF GALILEE.

HEY, JESUS IS COMING!

LET'S SPREAD THE NEWS.

SHORTLY AFTER, PEOPLE CAME OUT TO MEET HIM, AND THEY BROUGHT WITH THEM MANY WHO WERE SICK.

PLEASE, LET ME ONLY TOUCH THE HEM OF YOUR CLOAK.

I'M HEALED!

ON THE OTHER SIDE, THE PEOPLE WERE LOOKING FOR JESUS BUT COULDN'T FIND HIM.

HE MUST BE ON THE OTHER SHORE. COME!

THESE PEOPLE ARE LOOKING FOR ME BECAUSE THEY WANT BREAD AND MIRACLES.

JESUS ENTERED THE SYNAGOGUE IN CAPERNAUM...

DO NOT SEEK THE FOOD THAT SPOILS. SEEK THE FOOD THAT ENDURES AND GIVES ETERNAL LIFE.

HOW DO WE DO THAT?

SEEK GOD AND BELIEVE THE ONE GOD SENT TO YOU. I AM GOD'S BREAD FROM HEAVEN.

I AM THE TRUE BREAD OF LIFE. I HAVE COME DOWN FROM HEAVEN TO GIVE LIFE TO THE WORLD.

BREAD FROM HEAVEN? HAS HE GONE MAD? ISN'T HE THE SON OF JOSEPH? HE'S NOT FROM HEAVEN.

THOSE WHO COME TO ME WILL NEVER GO HUNGRY OR THIRSTY, AND I WILL NEVER TURN AWAY ANYONE WHO COMES TO ME.

THEN HE ADDED,

UNLESS YOU EAT MY FLESH AND DRINK MY BLOOD, YOU HAVE NO LIFE IN YOU. BUT IF YOU DO EAT AND DRINK, I WILL RAISE YOU UP ON THE LAST DAY.

THE JEWS WERE COMPLETELY CONFUSED.

HOW CAN THIS MAN GIVE US HIS FLESH TO EAT?

MY LIFE IS FROM THE HEAVENLY FATHER. HE HAS SENT ME TO YOU BECAUSE THERE'S NO LIFE IN YOU. BUT IF YOU FEED ON ME AND MY WORDS, YOU WILL LIVE BECAUSE OF ME.

ESUS WAS STAY—NG IN A HOUSE HERE HE HOPED E COULD REST. OW THIS MOTHER, HO WASN'T EWISH, CAME O HIM.

MASTER, PLEASE HELP ME!

PLEASE DRIVE THE EVIL SPIRIT OUT OF MY DAUGHTER!

THE WOMAN KEPT BEGGING FOR HELP.

I WAS SENT TO THE PEOPLE OF ISRAEL.

IT ISN'T RIGHT TO TAKE THE CHILDRENS' FOOD AND THROW IT TO DOGS.

YES, MASTER, THAT'S TRUE. BUT IT'S ALSO TRUE THAT THE DOGS EAT THE CRUMBS THAT THE CHILDREN DROP ON THE FLOOR UNDER THE TABLE.

BECAUSE YOU HAVE SAID THIS, THE EVIL SPIRIT HAS ALREADY LEFT YOUR DAUGHTER.

WHEN THE WOMAN RE-TURNED TO THE HOUSE, SHE FOUND HER DAUGHTER COMPLETELY CALM AND WELL.

HI, MOM!

UPON THEIR ARRIVAL IN CAPERNAUM, SIMON PETER WAS APPROACHED BY ONE OF THE TEMPLE TAX OFFICIALS RESPONSIBLE FOR COLLECTING THE TAXES USED FOR THE UPKEEP OF THE TEMPLE. THIS TAX WAS TWO DAYS' WAGES, AND IT WAS PAID ANNUALLY BY EVERY MALE OLDER THAN 20 YEARS OF AGE.

Relationships and Forgiveness

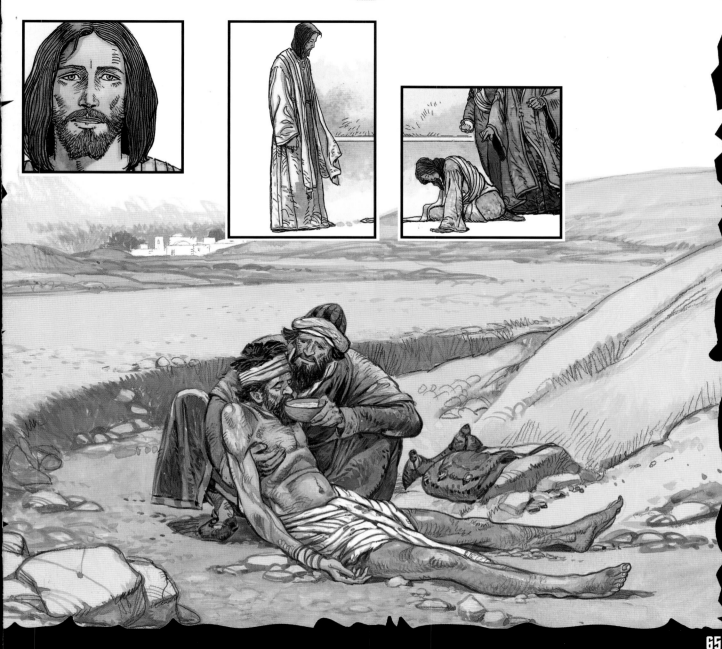

AGAIN AND AGAIN, JESUS HAD IMPRESSED ON THE DISCIPLES THE NECESSITY OF UNCONDITIONAL LOVE FOR EVERYONE, NOT JUST FOR ONE'S FRIENDS BUT FOR ONE'S ENEMIES AND PERSECUTORS AS WELL. YET IT STILL HADN'T DAWNED ON THE DISCIPLES WHAT HE REALLY MEANT.

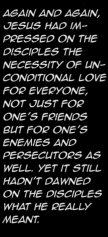

MASTER, EXCUSE ME, BUT EXACTLY HOW MUCH SHOULD I FORGIVE SOMEONE WHO CONSTANTLY SINS AGAINST ME? IS SEVEN TIMES ENOUGH?

NO, PETER, MULTIPLY IT BY SEVENTY, AND THAT WOULDN'T EVEN BE ENOUGH.

YOU STILL DON'T UNDERSTAND WHAT THE KINGDOM IS LIKE, DO YOU? THEN HEAR THIS STORY: THERE ONCE WAS A KING...

...WHO DECIDED TO UPDATE HIS ACCOUNTS.

THIS SERVANT STILL OWES ME TEN THOUSAND DOLLARS.

SELL HIM, HIS WIFE, AND CHILDREN AS SLAVES SO HIS DEBT CAN BE PAID.

SIR, PLEASE HAVE MERCY ON ME. I PROMISE I'LL PAY IT ALL BACK.

I FEEL PITY FOR YOU. I FORGIVE YOU.

YOUR DEBT IS CANCELED!

ON HIS WAY HOME, THIS SERVANT RAN INTO A MAN WHO OWED HIM TWO HUNDRED DOLLARS...

HEY, WAIT UP! YOU OWE ME MONEY!

PLEASE HAVE MERCY ON ME. I'LL PAY YOU BACK.

BUT THE CREDITOR WOULDN'T WAIT. HE PROSECUTED HIS DEBTOR AND HAD HIM PUT IN PRISON UNTIL THE DEBT WAS PAID IN FULL.

YOU WICKED SERVANT ...

THE OTHER SERVANTS IN THE KING'S HOUSEHOLD TOLD THE KING ABOUT IT.

THE POWER OF FORGIVENESS Matthew 18:21–35

SUKKOT, THE JEWISH FEAST OF TABERNACLES, WAS NEAR. EVERYONE EXPECTED JESUS TO GO TO JERUSALEM FOR THE FESTIVAL. MANY HOPED TO SEE A MIRACLE OR RECEIVE HEALING. JESUS WAITED FOR HIS RELATIVES TO LEAVE, THEN HE WENT IN SECRET.

THEY SAY JESUS IS HERE. BUT WHERE IS HE?

SOME THOUGHT JESUS WAS SENT BY GOD; OTHERS THOUGHT HE WAS A FAKE.

HE'S A GOOD PERSON. HOW CAN YOU SAY HE'S A MADMAN?

HALFWAY THROUGH THE FEAST JESUS ENTERED THE TEMPLE AND BEGAN TO TEACH IN PUBLIC.

AMAZING! WHERE DID JESUS LEARN ALL THIS? HE DIDN'T GO TO OUR SCHOOLS.

I DO NOT TEACH MY OWN IDEAS OR YOURS. MY TEACHING COMES FROM GOD WHO SENT ME. I DON'T SEEK MY OWN GLORY BUT GOD'S. WHY DO YOU PLOT TO KILL ME?

I KNOW GOD, BUT YOU DON'T. I CAME FROM HIM. HE APPROVES OF ME.

WHO WANTS TO KILL YOU?

HE THINKS HE'S THE MESSIAH.

HE'S EVIL.

WHEN THE PRIESTS AND THE PHARISEES HEARD THE CROWD ARGUING, THEY SENT THE TEMPLE GUARDS TO ARREST JESUS.

WHEN THE MESSIAH COMES, WILL HE DO MORE MIRACLES THAN THIS MAN?

BUT MOST OF THE COMMON PEOPLE BELIEVED HIM.

I THINK HE'S THE CHRIST, INDEED.

IF ANYONE IS THIRSTY, LET HIM COME TO ME AND DRINK. WHOEVER BELIEVES IN ME, STREAMS OF LIVING WATER SHALL FLOW FROM HIS INMOST BEING.

LET'S GET OUT OF HERE.

THE SOLDIERS RETURNED...

WHERE'S JESUS? YOU WERE SUPPOSED TO ARREST HIM!

WE'VE NEVER HEARD ANYBODY SPEAK LIKE HIM.

SO HE LED YOU ASTRAY TOO?

TAKE IT EASY! IT ISN'T LEGAL TO CONVICT A MAN WITHOUT A TRIAL FIRST.

BUT HE'S FROM GALILEE. SCRIPTURE SAYS THAT THE MESSIAH WILL COME FROM KING DAVID'S FAMILY AND TOWN!

ONE DAY WHEN JESUS WAS TEACHING IN THE TEMPLE, A LAW EXPERT WANTED TO TEST HIM.

TEACHER, WHAT MUST I DO TO HAVE ETERNAL LIFE IN HEAVEN?

WHAT DOES THE LAW SAY?

ALL YOUR HEART, SOUL, STRENGTH, AND MIND, AND LOVE YOUR NEIGH-BOR AS YOURSELF.

YOU'RE RIGHT. DO THIS AND YOU WILL LIVE.

BUT WHO IS MY NEIGHBOR?

LISTEN CAREFULLY TO THIS STORY:

A MAN WAS TRAVELING FROM HERE TO JERICHO.

SUDDENLY HE WAS ATTACKED BY THIEVES.

THE THIEVES STRIPPED HIM OF HIS CLOTHES AND BEAT HIM UP.

THEN THEY LEFT HIM HALF DEAD ON THE ROADSIDE.

A LITTLE LATER A PRIEST CAME BY. HE SAW THE MAN...

...AND PASSED BY.

THEN CAME A LEVITE. HE ALSO PASSED BY.

DINNER, [J]ESUS [S]AW HOW [S]OME OF [T]HE GUESTS [W]ERE QUICK [T]O CHOOSE [T]HE BEST [P]LACES [N]EAR THE [H]OST.

FEAST, DON'T CHOOSE THE BEST PLACE TO SIT.

IMPORTANT MAY HAVE BEEN INVITED TOO.

THIS SEAT IS RESERVED FOR THIS MAN. PLEASE LEAVE IT FOR HIM.

THE LOWEST PLACE...

...SO THAT YOUR HOST WILL COME AND SAY, "PLEASE, COME TO A BETTER PLACE!"

THIS WILL BRING YOU HONOR IN THE PRESENCE OF THE OTHER GUESTS.

AND YOU, MY HOST, WHEN YOU GIVE A DINNER, DON'T JUST INVITE THOSE WHO CAN INVITE YOU BACK.

NO, INVITE THE POOR, THE CRIPPLED, THE LAME, AND THE BLIND. THIS MAY NOT BRING YOU HONOR, BUT IT WILL BLESS YOU SO MUCH MORE.

HEAR THIS STORY: A CERTAIN MAN WAS PRE-PARING A GREAT BANQUET AND INVITED MANY PEOPLE THEN HE SENT OUT HIS SERVANT...

PLEASE COME TO MY MASTER'S BANQUET!

BUT THEY GAVE ALL KINDS OF EXCUSES.

SORRY, I'M BUSY. I CAN'T COME.

ONE SAID HE'D JUST BOUGHT A NEW FIELD, ANOTHER THAT HE'D JUST BOUGHT NEW LIVESTOCK, A THIRD THAT HE'D JUST BEEN MARRIED...

MASTER, NO ONE COULD COME TO YOUR BANQUET.

THEN HURR[Y] OUT INTO TH[E] STREETS AN[D] ALLEYS OF T[HE] TOWN AND INV[ITE] THE POOR, T[HE] CRIPPLED, TH[E] BLIND, AND T[HE] LAME!

AND SO HE DID.

FINALLY, THE HOUSE WAS FULL.

MASTER, THERE'S STILL ROOM FOR MORE PEOPLE.

VERY WELL THEN, GO ON THE HIGHWAYS AND BYWAYS, AND INVITE EVERYONE YOU MEET.

THEN THE MAN SAID, "NONE OF THOSE FIRST INVITED WILL TASTE THE FEAST I HAVE PREPARED."

Discipleship in Action

THE LOST SON WHO RETURNED HOME Luke 15:11–28

THE RICH MAN COULD EAT EVERYTHING HE DESIRED, WHILE LAZARUS HAD TO EAT THE LEFTOVERS FROM HIS TABLE. LAZARUS' BODY WAS COVERED WITH SORES, AND WILD DOGS WOULD LICK HIS SORES.

ONE DAY LAZARUS DIED, AND THE ANGELS OF GOD CARRIED HIM AWAY AND LAID HIM IN ABRAHAM'S ARMS.

THE RICH MAN ALSO DIED...

...AND WENT TO THE PLACE OF DEATH. FROM THERE HE COULD SEE LAZARUS AND ABRAHAM FAR OFF.

ALSO, BETWEEN YOU AND US IS A HUGE PIT THAT NO ONE CAN CROSS.

THEN SEND LAZARUS TO WARN MY FIVE BROTHERS SO THEY WON'T END UP IN THIS PLACE OF SUFFERING.

IF THEY WON'T LISTEN TO THE SCRIPTURES, A MESSENGER FROM THE DEAD WILL NOT CONVINCE THEM EITHER.

THEY ALREADY HAVE THE LAW OF MOSES AND THE WRITINGS OF THE PROPHETS. LET THEM LISTEN TO THEM.

IN LIFE YOU SPENT YOUR TIME IN LUXURY AND FUN. NOW IT'S LAZARUS' TURN TO ENJOY ETERNAL LIFE.

FATHER ABRAHAM, I'M IN GREAT PAIN. PLEASE HELP ME! SEND LAZARUS TO DIP HIS FINGER IN WATER AND COOL MY TONGUE.

BUT THEY'LL ONLY LISTEN AND REPENT IF SOMEONE COMES BACK FROM THE DEAD AND WARNS THEM.

A FEW MINUTES LATER, A YOUNG MAN CAME RUNNING AND BOWED DOWN BEFORE JESUS...

RABBI!

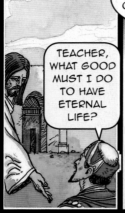

TEACHER, WHAT GOOD MUST I DO TO HAVE ETERNAL LIFE?

WHY ASK ME ABOUT GOOD? ONLY GOD IS GOOD.

IF YOU WANT ETERNAL LIFE -- KEEP THE COMMANDMENTS OF MOSES.

I HAVE KEPT THEM ALL SINCE CHILDHOOD.

THERE'S STILL ONE THING YO[U] MUST DO. GO AND SE[LL] ALL YOU OWN, AND GIVE THE MONEY TO THE POOR.

THEN COME AND FOLLOW ME.

THE RICH YOUNG MAN TURNED AROUND AND WENT AWAY SAD.

IT'S VERY HARD FOR A RICH PERSON TO ENTER GOD'S KINGDOM. IT'S EASIER FOR A CAMEL TO GO THROUGH THE EYE OF A NEEDLE.

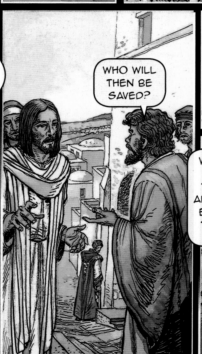

WHO WILL THEN BE SAVED?

FOR HUMANS IT'S IMPOSSIBLE. BUT WITH[ ] GOD EVERYTHING IS POSSIBLE.

WHAT ABOUT US, MAS-TER? WE'VE ALREADY LEFT EVERYTHING TO FOLLOW YOU.

YOU WILL GET A HUNDRED TIMES MORE THAN YOU LEF[T] BEHIND--AND RECEIVE ETERNAL LIFE.

DON'T WORRY. EVERYONE WILL HAVE A CHANCE. HEAR THIS PARABLE AND YOU'LL BETTER UNDER-STAND HOW GOD WORKS:

A LANDOWNER WENT OUT EARLY IN THE MORNING TO HIRE WORKERS FOR HIS VINEYARD. HE AGREED TO PAY EACH A SILVER COIN FOR ONE DAY'S WORK.

JESUS HEALS A BLIND MAN Luke 18:35—43

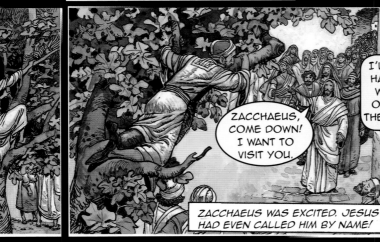

THE WEDDING BANQUET Matthew 21:33–46; 22:1–14

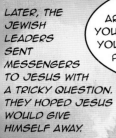

LATER, THE JEWISH LEADERS SENT MESSENGERS TO JESUS WITH A TRICKY QUESTION. THEY HOPED JESUS WOULD GIVE HIMSELF AWAY.

TEACHER, YOU ARE AN HONEST MAN. YOU TELL THE TRUTH AND YOU DON'T CARE ABOUT PEOPLE'S OPINION OF YOU.

TELL US; SHOULD WE PAY TAXES TO CAESAR OR NOT?

JESUS KNEW THEY WERE TRYING TO TRICK HIM. IF HE SAID YES, THEY WOULD ACCUSE HIM OF BEING PRO-ROMAN.

IF HE SAID NO, THE ROMANS COULD RIGHTLY ACCUSE HIM OF RESISTING THE ROMAN RULERS.

PSSST! WE'VE GOT HIM NOW!

BRING ME A SILVER COIN. LET ME SEE IT.

SO THEY HANDED JESUS A SILVER COIN.

TELL ME WHOSE PICTURE AND NAME ARE ON THIS COIN?

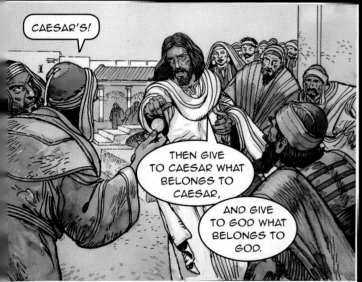

CAESAR'S!

THEN GIVE TO CAESAR WHAT BELONGS TO CAESAR,

AND GIVE TO GOD WHAT BELONGS TO GOD.

THE MEN WERE ASTONISHED BY JESUS' ANSWER.

THE SADDUCEES WERE NEXT TO TRY HIM.

TEACHER, THE LAW SAYS THAT IF A MAN DIES, HIS BROTHER MUST MARRY HIS WIDOW AND TAKE CARE OF HER.

URRGH!

NOW THERE WERE SEVEN BROTHERS. THEY ALL DIED ONE AFTER ANOTHER AND LEFT THE FIRST BROTHER'S WIFE TO THE NEXT BROTHER AND SO ON UNTIL SHE FINALLY DIED, TOO.

TELL US; WHOSE WIFE WILL SHE BE IN HEAVEN?

YOU IGNORANT PEOPLE! YOU HAVE NO IDEA WHAT HEAVEN IS LIKE. IN HEAVEN PEOPLE DON'T MARRY.

THEY LIVE FOREVER WITH GOD.

THE JEWISH LEADERS TRY TO TRICK JESUS

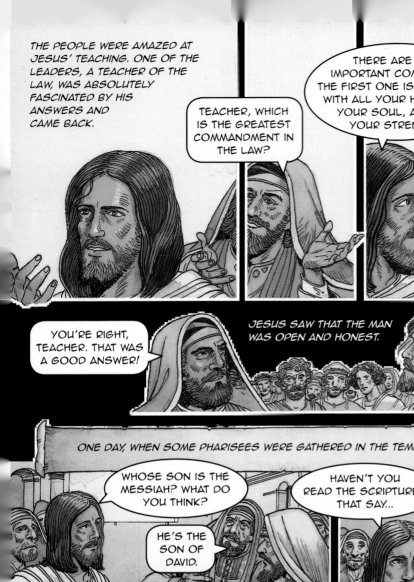

THE PEOPLE WERE AMAZED AT JESUS' TEACHING. ONE OF THE LEADERS, A TEACHER OF THE LAW, WAS ABSOLUTELY FASCINATED BY HIS ANSWERS AND CAME BACK.

TEACHER, WHICH IS THE GREATEST COMMANDMENT IN THE LAW?

THERE ARE TWO IMPORTANT COMMANDS. THE FIRST ONE IS LOVE GOD WITH ALL YOUR HEART, ALL YOUR SOUL, AND ALL YOUR STRENGTH.

THE SECOND IS LOVE OTHERS THE SAME WAY YOU LOVE YOURSELF.

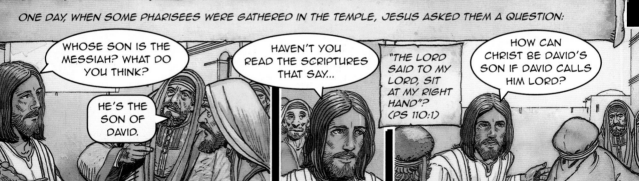

YOU'RE RIGHT, TEACHER. THAT WAS A GOOD ANSWER!

JESUS SAW THAT THE MAN WAS OPEN AND HONEST.

MY FRIEND, YOU ARE NOT FAR FROM GOD'S KINGDOM.

AFTER THIS, THEY WERE AFRAID TO ASK JESUS ANY MORE TRICKY QUESTIONS.

ONE DAY, WHEN SOME PHARISEES WERE GATHERED IN THE TEMPLE, JESUS ASKED THEM A QUESTION:

WHOSE SON IS THE MESSIAH? WHAT DO YOU THINK?

HE'S THE SON OF DAVID.

HAVEN'T YOU READ THE SCRIPTURES THAT SAY...

"THE LORD SAID TO MY LORD, SIT AT MY RIGHT HAND"? (PS 110:1)

HOW CAN CHRIST BE DAVID'S SON IF DAVID CALLS HIM LORD?

THE PHARISEES DIDN'T KNOW WHAT TO SAY, SO JESUS TURNED TO THE PEOPLE AROUND HIM.

DO WHAT YOUR RELIGIOUS LEADERS TELL YOU. BUT DON'T FOLLOW THEIR EXAMPLE BECAUSE THEY DON'T PRACTICE WHAT THEY PREACH. THEY LOVE TO BE SEEN AND RESPECTED, YET THEY PUT HEAVY BURDENS ON YOUR SHOULDERS. BUT I TELL YOU...

...THE GREATEST AMONG YOU WILL BE YOUR SERVANT AND YOU WILL KNOW HIM BY HIS HUMILITY, NOT BY GREAT HONORS.

WOE TO YOU HYPOCRITES! YOU SLAM THE DOOR OF GOD'S KINGDOM IN PEOPLE'S FACES, AND YOU DON'T ENTER IN YOURSELVES.

The Price of True Love

Death and Resurrection

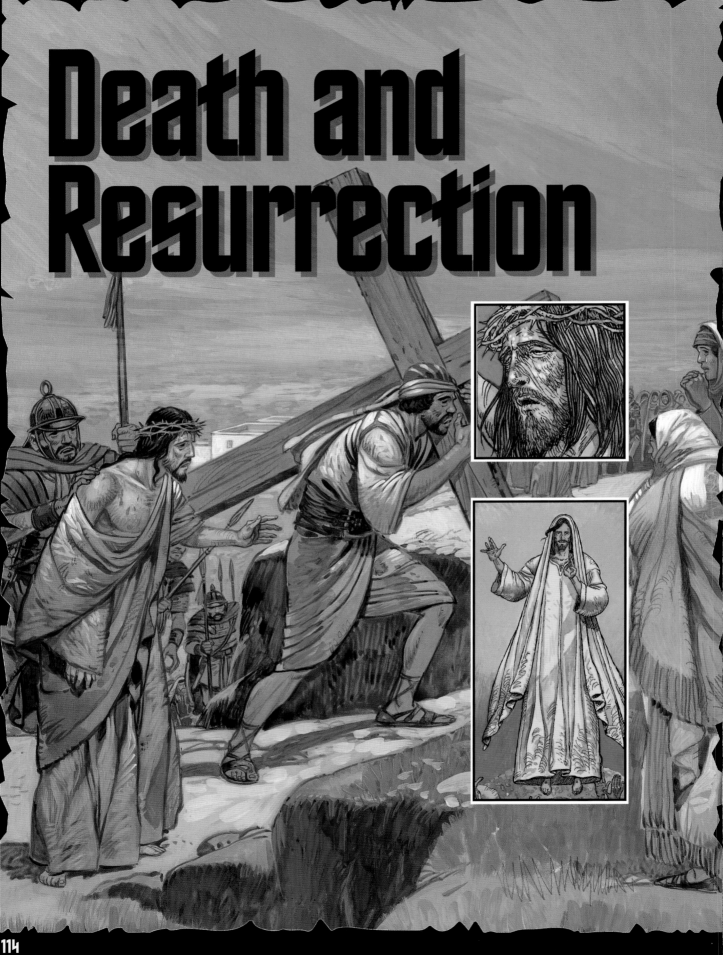

BUT WHAT'S HIS CRIME?

CRUCIFY HIM!

YOU ARE RESPONSIBLE FOR THIS. I'M INNOCENT OF THIS MAN'S DEATH.

UNCONTROLLABLE. HE WAS AFRAID THEY WOULD START A RIOT.

LET HIS BLOOD COME UPON US AND OUR CHILDREN!

WHEN JUDAS ISCARIOT HEARD THAT JESUS HAD BEEN SENTENCED TO DEATH BECAUSE HE HAD BETRAYED JESUS, JUDAS REALIZED HIS SIN.

CRUCIFY JESUS!

WHAT HAVE I DONE?

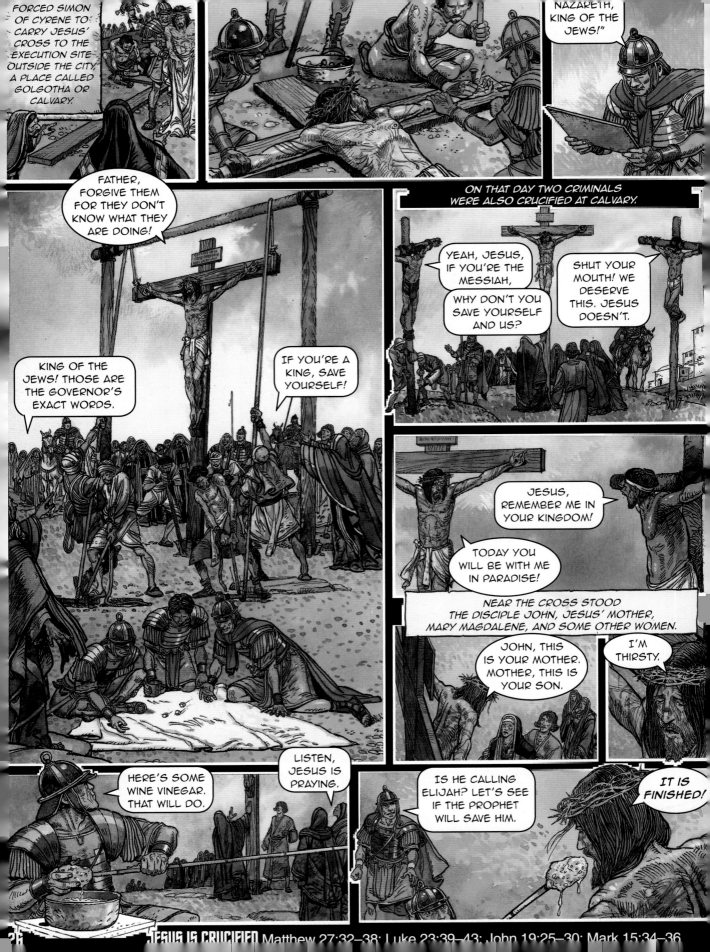

FORCED SIMON OF CYRENE TO CARRY JESUS' CROSS TO THE EXECUTION SITE OUTSIDE THE CITY, A PLACE CALLED GOLGOTHA OR CALVARY.

NAZARETH, KING OF THE JEWS!"

FATHER, FORGIVE THEM FOR THEY DON'T KNOW WHAT THEY ARE DOING!

KING OF THE JEWS! THOSE ARE THE GOVERNOR'S EXACT WORDS.

IF YOU'RE A KING, SAVE YOURSELF!

ON THAT DAY TWO CRIMINALS WERE ALSO CRUCIFIED AT CALVARY.

YEAH, JESUS, IF YOU'RE THE MESSIAH,

WHY DON'T YOU SAVE YOURSELF AND US?

SHUT YOUR MOUTH! WE DESERVE THIS. JESUS DOESN'T.

JESUS, REMEMBER ME IN YOUR KINGDOM!

TODAY YOU WILL BE WITH ME IN PARADISE!

NEAR THE CROSS STOOD THE DISCIPLE JOHN, JESUS' MOTHER, MARY MAGDALENE, AND SOME OTHER WOMEN.

JOHN, THIS IS YOUR MOTHER. MOTHER, THIS IS YOUR SON.

I'M THIRSTY.

HERE'S SOME WINE VINEGAR. THAT WILL DO.

LISTEN, JESUS IS PRAYING.

IS HE CALLING ELIJAH? LET'S SEE IF THE PROPHET WILL SAVE HIM.

IT IS FINISHED!

WE'LL BURY THE MASTER IN THE TOMB I'VE HAD CUT FOR MYSELF.

SOME WOMEN WHO HAD FOLLOWED HIM CAME WITH SPICES AND PERFUMES FOR THE BODY OF JESUS.

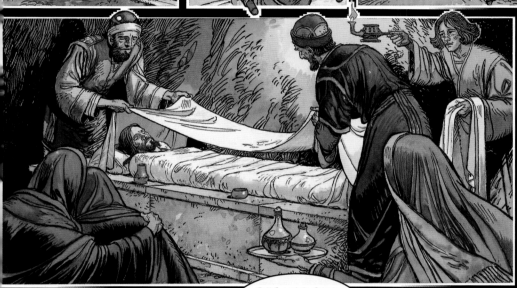

AFTER THIS THEY CLOSED THE ENTRANCE.

THE NEXT DAY SOME OF THE PRIESTS AND PHARISEES CAME TO PILATE AND ASKED HIM TO SEAL THE TOMB AND HAVE IT GUARDED DAY AND NIGHT.

THIS LIAR SAID HE'D COME BACK TO LIFE AFTER THREE DAYS.

YEAH, HIS FOLLOWERS MAY COME AND STEAL HIS BODY.

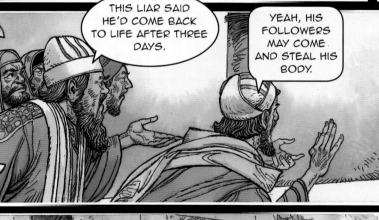

SO THEY SEALED THE TOMB SECURELY TO PREVENT THE DISCIPLES FROM STEALING THE BODY AND CLAIMING AFTERWARD THAT JESUS HAD RISEN FROM THE DEAD.

IN THE MEANTIME THE GUARDS RETURNED TO THE CITY TO REPORT WHAT HAD HAPPENED. THE CHIEF PRIESTS WERE ALARMED. THEY KNEW THIS COULD MEAN EXTRA TROUBLE AND CAUSE THE ROMAN GOVERNOR, PILATE, TO INTERFERE WITH HIS SOLDIERS.

GONE? WHAT DO YOU MEAN?

WE'LL MAKE SURE YOU WON'T BE PUNISHED!

THAT'S RIDICULOUS!

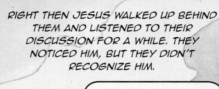

LOOK! IF YOU GO OUT AND TELL THE PEOPLE THAT HIS DISCIPLES CAME AND STOLE THE BODY IN THE NIGHT,...

...WE'LL PAY YOU THIS MONEY.

THE GUARDS WENT OUT AND SPREAD THIS LIE, AND SOME PEOPLE HAVE BELIEVED IT EVER SINCE.

THAT SAME DAY TWO DISCIPLES WERE ON THEIR WAY TO A SMALL VILLAGE CALLED EMMAUS.

JESUS DIED. NOW THE WOMEN ARE SAYING HE'S ALIVE?!

I DON'T KNOW WHAT TO THINK.

RIGHT THEN JESUS WALKED UP BEHIND THEM AND LISTENED TO THEIR DISCUSSION FOR A WHILE. THEY NOTICED HIM, BUT THEY DIDN'T RECOGNIZE HIM.

HAVEN'T YOU HEARD? JESUS OF NAZARETH WAS SENTENCED TO DEATH BY THE JEWISH LEADERS AND CRUCIFIED BY THE ROMANS. THEY DIDN'T REALIZE HE WAS A GREAT PROPHET WHO SPOKE WITH AUTHORITY AND GREAT POWER.

WHAT ARE YOU TALKING ABOUT?

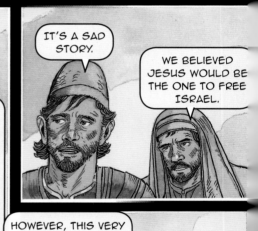

IT'S A SAD STORY.

WE BELIEVED JESUS WOULD BE THE ONE TO FREE ISRAEL.

HOWEVER, THIS VERY MORNING SOME OF HIS DISCIPLES CLAIM THAT HIS BODY IS GONE. THEY EVEN SAW ANGELS ON THE GRAVE.

HAVEN'T YOU READ THE PROPHETS?

THE ROAD TO

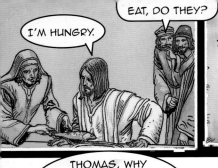

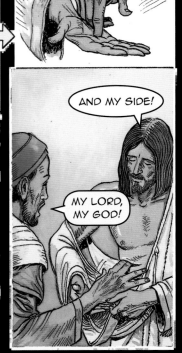

LATER, JESUS APPEARED TO SEVEN OF THE DISCIPLES. PETER WANTED TO GO FISHING, AND THE OTHERS JOINED HIM. AFTER FISHING ALL NIGHT, THEY CAME BACK TO SHORE EARLY IN THE MORNING.

THIS HAS BEEN THE STORY OF THE LIFE OF JESUS, FROM HIS BIRTH TO HIS GOING UP TO HEAVEN. HE IS ALIVE AND HAS PROMISED TO RETURN.

THE STORY CONTINUES!